Wilf climbed on the swing.

3

Chip pushed Wilf.

Floppy looked at the rope.

5

Biff climbed on the swing.

Floppy barked and barked.

Chip climbed on the swing.

Floppy barked and barked and barked.

Kipper went on the swing.

'What a silly dog!' said Kipper.

Wilma went on too.

'What a silly dog!' said Wilma.

The children went home.

14

Floppy looked at the rope.

Splash!
Oh no!

16